ON THE LINE

The *WARD* cartoons from RAILNEWS

www.crecy.co.uk

Compiled by Kevin Robertson

© Crecy Publishing Ltd 2016

ISBN 9781909328372

First published in 2016 by Crécy Publishing

A CIP record for this book is available from the British Library

Printed in the UK by Latimer Trend

Crécy Publishing Limited
1a Ringway Trading Estate
Shadowmoss Road
Manchester M22 5LH

www.crecy.co.uk

Foreword

The Ward cartoons were a product of the railways at a time when a 'new image' was being presented.

Gone were 150 years of steam and everything that went with it and instead it was a case of new trains, new colours, new uniforms and new initiatives. *Railnews* and in their own way the Ward cartoons were one means of describing these changes to the workforce even if some of the initiatives shown may appear both strange and outmoded today.

If there was a failing with rail publicity of the time it was simply that these same cartoons were aimed at a limited audience, the railway staff. Had they been made more widely available what the railway was trying to achieve might well have been better understood by the general public.

I am delighted to provide a foreword for this book of cartoons and commend both their comedy and the message portrayed to a wider audience.

Sir William McAlpine

Introduction

For more than a decade *RAILNEWS*, the in-house staff magazine for British Railways, included in its monthly issues a topical cartoon penned under the name WARD.

While individual humour is of course subjective, the drawings produced nevertheless managed to bridge the gap between contemporary day-to-day life, politics, news of the day, and of course 'in-house' situations. As such they form a unique record of contemporary life – and especially rail travel – during the period.

If you were a passenger during the late 1960s through to the early 1980s (the word 'customer' was not then being used), you will certainly recognise many of the scenes depicted. Travel, ticketing, overcrowding, ancillary services – Motorail, Travellers Fare, etc – all feature, as do new trains, electrification and of course seasonal topics.

The following pages show what is was really like when the everyday slogan was 'We're getting there' – trouble was, they never told us where 'there' was!

The cartoons themselves, of which this is but a selection, also form what we can now see is a comedic way of introducing new technology and innovation, starting right at the front on page 6, where 'health and safety' has even infiltrated the ticket office. (See also page 32 for 'health and safety' as applicable to a passenger as well! Other similar views with 'high-vis' workwear are on pages 50 and 51.)

We also have the innovations of the time, such as 'Freightliner' on page 7 followed by 'Red Star' parcels on the next page 8. In the case of the latter it also allows a take on the Russian regime.

It is difficult to single out favourites, but one must be page 10. This shows the interior of a new panel signal box but with a mechanical frame in the background, which was available for emergencies. This particular drawing obviously struck a chord with some signalmen as I recall seeing a copy pinned up in a signal box that was about to close, to be replaced by a panel. See also page 36, depicting an incident in another modern panel signal box.

Most of the drawings, however, are self-explanatory, but there are also some where Ward was perhaps slightly off-key. Take page 13, for example, which has in the background posters for the inauguration of the Bournemouth Electrification in July 1967 and the comment 'New Train Times...' accompanied by an irate City gent complaining that he was unaware. Here Ward has missed the point in that the train should of course have been shown in modern blue livery. Even so, it is also a pointer to human nature in that familiarity breeds contempt and, probably no matter how many posters and leaflets had been displayed or were available, some passengers would never get the message.

We move ahead in time now – literally – to the advent of Network SouthEast and the various standard fittings that were later adopted throughout the system. In the case of page 16 it is the digital clock that is the feature. Conformity yes, but perhaps not blind obedience.

Political satire also played a part in the undated image shown on page 17. This was when the Common Market had been renamed the EEC – the rest, as they say, speaks for itself. Incidentally – and nothing whatsoever to do with the Ward cartoons – prior to his death Sir Winston Churchill had left instructions that his funeral train must depart from Waterloo and not from the more logical Paddington – a swipe, it was said, by the great man at our French neighbours.

Change is an ongoing feature of any transport system, one such incident being the demise of the all-Pullman 'Brighton Belle' in 1972 on page 19. For many years the train operated in its iconic umber and cream Pullman livery – somehow it never quite looked right in Corporate blue/grey – with each Pullman car (Pullmans were always 'cars', never 'carriages') given a name. In this particular drawing we see a railwayman distraught at the loss of the train and its named cars, although his named goods wagons would also not last long under the move towards block trains.

Page 21 depicts another lost feature, the wheel-tapper. At certain stations main-line trains would have a man hitting each wheel with his hammer, the purpose being to see that the resulting sound was a 'ring'; a dull 'thud' would indicate a wheel/tyre defect and the vehicle would be removed from the train.

Sexism also played a part in contemporary advertising – on page 22 neither the 'Ladies only' excursion nor the cross-dressing man would nowadays be permitted to be displayed in the way shown. (A similar 'non-PC' cartoon is shown on page 60.)

Page 24 is another favourite, showing two features that have now all but disappeared. The first is the transport of prisoners by train – Waterloo to Plymouth or Okehampton (for Dartmoor) was a regular move, although normally a compartment was used. Who might also recall the steward coming round enquiring as to which sitting for dinner 'Sir' might prefer? (In reality this would often depend on how far 'Sir' was travelling.) But then who could have foreseen the move towards a trolley-only buffet service...?

To railway personnel and enthusiasts alike, page 25 will be self-explanatory but, just in case, it was generally a requirement for the driver to contact the signalman if he was held at a red signal for any length of time (although there were and still are exceptions). Imagine said driver's consternation when instead of speaking to the signalman he was put through to the speaking clock! Crossed wires perhaps?

Page 27 shows a chef (or waiter) clearly stressed and in need of more time, hence his gratitude at having his train slowed down by permanent way work.

And slowing down was obviously what the porter wanted in the next view on page 28, but clearly wasn't going to get. Probably a reference to the new InterCity 125 (HST) trains, which could indeed play havoc with anything not secured when passing at speed. The now familiar yellow lines on platforms indicating 'do not cross' are not there solely for decoration.

Not unnaturally there are a number of references to the Channel Tunnel in the cartoons, both before and immediately after opening. After all, nothing like it had even been seen and it is perhaps not surprising that were was ignorance and confusion amongst staff – see page 33 (as well as pages 40 and 41]).

Another aspect we nowadays take for granted is 'IT', or computers. I suspect all of us 'of a certain age' can recall the scepticism or even fear that was generated by those first machines, and there was no reason why the railway should have been any different. Hence that shown on page 35, even if today the reaction we express is almost one of sympathy rather perhaps than amusement. (As here, Ward produced a few of his works in simple black and white – why this should have been is not certain.)

Rarely it seems did Ward take a swipe at the approaching era of railway privatisation, but we certainly have it on page 38. To the Victorian railwaymen the idea of a nationalised rail network would have seemed anathema, preferring instead to consider the thought that their own system would gobble up its neighbours, as indeed was often the case. The other aspect of this particular drawing is the suggestions box, something the pre-nationalisation companies encouraged, as indeed did the nationalised British Railways, with prizes being awarded for good or adopted ideas. Privatisation of sorts also features on page 39 – or perhaps it should be plain old-fashioned capitalism... see also page 70.

While the High Speed Train was and indeed continues to be a success for both British Rail and many of the current privatised operators, sadly the reverse was the case for the APT (Advanced Passenger Train). The train would feature in at least three Ward drawings on pages 42 and 43, although why the variant in the shape of a hydrofoil is not quite understood.

Page 44 is another favourite and, despite the caption, has absolutely nothing to do with harsh braking. Instead these were a new design of tank car (yes, tank wagons were also known as 'cars') where the provision of a slope allowed for ease of bottom discharge: the driver and his mate need not then be alarmed, even though in the days of the 'old-timer' harsh braking could indeed do all sorts of damage.

On page 45, for *Opportunity Knocks* please read the 21st-century equivalent – *Britain's Got Talent*, *The X Factor* or similar.

Any comment about page 48 runs the risk of your compiler being whisked away to the Tower, as this is all about HM Queen and the Duke of Edinburgh and the first electric train over the full length of the West Coast Main Line. The Duke was of course a lover of speed... Page 49 shows another electrification image, this time with the porter having built a scaffold to tap into the overhead electricity supply when it arrives at his station – it is missing at the moment. But poor George – 25kV is a bit different from what he will get out of his plug in the mess room.

Branded wagons and likewise private-owner vehicles were something that disappeared from the scene for some years, that is until people like Foster Yeoman reinvented the idea. Clearly page 53 is a Christmas issue – well, it does save the reindeer some work.

Sadly, despite the utopia expressed on page 56, rail travel can at times nowadays be similar to that shown on the roadway beneath the train. 'Let the train take the strain' was the slogan – well, we did. The result nowadays if often overcrowding and frustrated and angry passengers. Perhaps we need to refresh our memories of the Japanese method of employing 'People Pushers', as joked at earlier on page 14. Even so, there have been initiatives over the years to encourage ever more 'bums on seats' – 'Rail Riders', 'Network Card', etc, etc – see page 61.

'Dial-a-Train' (page 63 is a slight puzzle. It cannot have been meant to be taken literally; the only idea we can come up with is for booking party travel ... any ideas?

Who cannot recall 'Travellers Fare'? Let it be said that sometimes it was very good indeed and at others – well, the era of a curled-up edge to the BR sandwich can still be recalled decades later. The era of the footplateman's fry-up is first referred to on page 64, while alongside page 65 is an exercise in pure nostalgia – for one passenger at least – referring to the days when a three- or even four-course meal, freshly cooked on board, was available to be served. And silver service, of course...

Customer care was a regular subject for Ward; indeed, we may wonder what influence British Rail actually had over the subjects depicted in the cartoons. So far as page 69 is concerned, we can safely say 'not a lot'. A complaint of assault at the very least comes to mind instead.

Another favourite (but then who of 'Railnews' generation cannot have been a fan of 'Dad's Army' either?). Twenty-six years separated D-Day in 1945 from the day of the same name in 1971, the latter not referring to invasion but instead the end of the era of shillings and pence and their replacement with 'new pence'. The BR emblem on the shoulder of the old soldier on page 71 is a neat touch.

Finally on page 72 'Road-Rail Integration was the ideal. Today it is certainly better than it was, but in many places there is still some way to go.

The publishers and compiler would like to thank 'Railnews' and in particular Sim Harris, for their permission to reproduce the Ward images, Messrs Ian Allan Ltd., and also Sir William McAlpine for kindly agreeing to provide the introduction.

Kevin Robertson

"She refuses to go to the Royal Wedding on that train ... she says when she went to Queen Victoria's Jubilee the engine had a proper chimney."

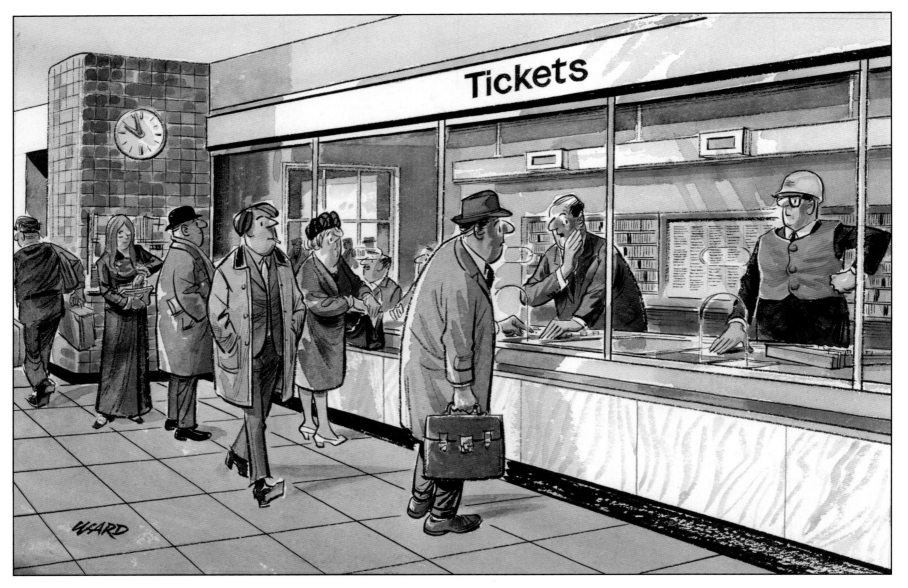

"*He's very safety-conscious - once caught his thumb in a ticket machine*"

"He says it's jolly decent of us to paint it in his livery."

"He says 'Rockets, nyet ... quickest way to anywhere is glorious British Rail Red Star Express Service.'"

"Two and a half returns to Penzance, and I'm about fed up with this one ... can we send him Red Star?"

"He says they don't really want to go to London, but it would be sinful to pass up a bargain like this!"

"Drive in, lad ... we've never had one shrink in the wash yet!"

"Why didn't somebody TELL me!"

"It's the latest equipment for commuter routes - one packs 'em in, the other gets 'em out."

"Keenly observant, the British. Of 78 through the barrier, 77 said, ' Morning ... wet day'."

"One up on St. Pancras - our Victorian digital clock."

"Charlie's gone all E.E.C. ... as a gesture to our French partners he wants to re-name Waterloo station."

" What d' you mean, ' Expressing their disappointment and frustration` ... This lot's team won."

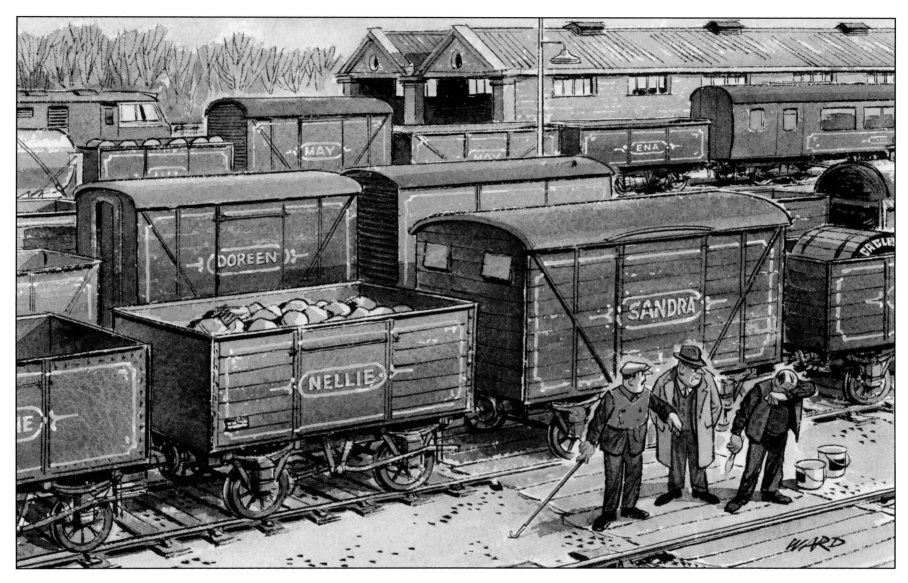

"He just can't forget the Brighton Belle."

"This gentleman would like to congratulate BR on all the renovations,
and can he book for the first Stately Stations tour?"

"If it wasn't for this one, we could play Good King Wenceslas."

" Another gatecrasher on the Ladies Midweek Shopping Special ... they go to all that trouble, then give the game away by coming back loaded with fishing rods and tape recorders."

"He says he thought it was a multi-storey car park – until it moved."

"You take first dinner and I'll take second ... OK?"

"At the third stroke it will be..."

"Don't know what it is about old Bill but somehow, even off duty, you can tell he's a shunter."

"Platelayers ... thank goodness! I've got 84 to lay before lunch and my mate's off sick."

"No matter what the slipstream does to our dahlias, we can't interfere with the running of the Express!"

"Enjoy the Test Match, Sir Gregory. Have I your word of honour
that you won't slash the cushions if England lose?"

"Train Spotters' complaint ... they haven't time to get the number of a train before the next one's in."

"I don't know whether to enter it under 'Full length pictures of attractive girls' or 'Railway activity.'"

"Somebody once ran into him with a baggage trolley ..."

"Bert, the Chunnel's lit all the way through, and it doesn't happen till 1980!"

"Disgusting state these carriages are in
... BR ought to be ashamed!"

"I indented for microcomputers - not microcommuters!"

"We're getting interference from Houston control - it looks like Apollo 12
is just passing Hemel Hempstead."

"... if we insist ... but if he can't wear his hat the whole deals off."

" And Master Clever Porter Perkins here suggests that all tha companies might merge into one national railway, which he would call British Rail!"

"Dad says a railway needs investment - so, 5p or you don't play."

" I told you the Channel Tunnel was on again — Freds getting a flying start."

"He thinks he may have missed a signal somewhere ... wants to know if he's all right for Dusseldorf."

"That's what I call passenger care ... building in a nine degree tilt for the fast bends just so's their tea won't slop over."

"Terrible what harsh braking can do to wagons!"

" ....Betty, I've told you before, you're not suppose to practice for your Opportunity Knocks audition here!"

"You're wating your time, Bert ... they've got no vacancies!"

"My husband's so proud of driving the HST."

"If you-know-who gets to these controls he'll make the HST look like the Slow Boat to China!"

"When electrification comes he's determined to get his share."

" Bert reckons he's got added
protection - from low-flying
aircraft, baggage trolleys
and gravel rash."

" I don't care what the weather forecast says -
my corns tell me it's going to rain."

" He says it's a waste, wearing it only once a year ... with that on he can be seen for miles."

"He just loves Christmas – and don't worry, the reindeer is not on the payroll."

" Getting into BR Private Wagons is the best thing we ever did, Rudolf."

"He says he wants it undersealed!"

"All right dear, the 'Mr and Mrs British Rail' contest's finished you can ease up on the 'helpful and understanding' bit!"

"They might have told us they were reopening the station ... we've just got our potatoes in!"

"Have we a 'Motorist-who-just-can't-take-anymore' Railcard?"

"He says it's only a temporary modification of the uniform – until the World Cup's over."

"Heavens - don't say they've changed the uniform AGAIN."

"Here she comes ...' Good colour, nice bouquet, full-bodied and travels well'."

"Do you get the impression the Rail Rider Club could be planning a takeover ...?"

" Is that ACAS?"

"Yes, I did just ring Dial-a-Train ... ?"

"Quick, this is the one! I remember it ... you get a four course lunch for three-and-six."

"We've got to get rid of it somehow."

" When the high-density passenger coaches come in, we won't have to look far for the
first two high-density passengers!"

"With what joy, Edmund, must the gentlemen return to the pure air of the country after their day spent in foul pollution of the City!"

" I'm fulfilling our desire to identify with the passengers by helping him in ... besides, he makes the platform look untidy."

"It says 'All assets and staff transferred from BR to NFC' ... so we get the dartboard!"

" But, Bert ... it's not that sort of D-Day!"

" Road-rail integration's set in, then."